Explore
Biology
Beyond the Basics
STUDENT WORKBOOK

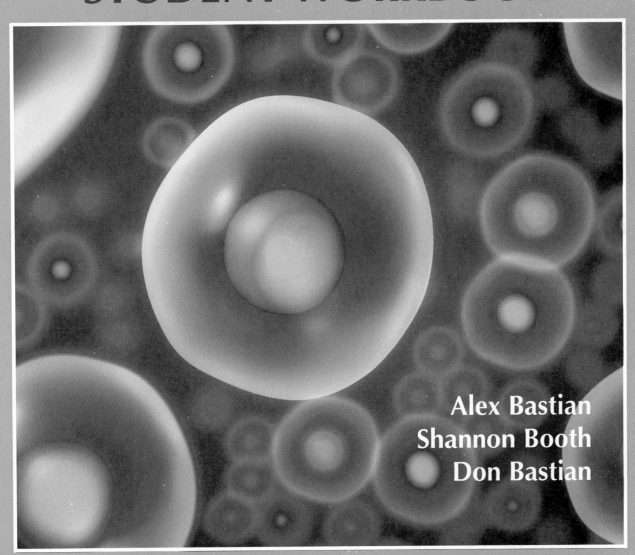

Alex Bastian
Shannon Booth
Don Bastian

Explore Biology
Student Book

By Alex Bastian, Shannon Booth, and Don Bastian
Edited by Shannon Booth
Art Direction by Beverly Sanders
Illustrations by Josh Eacret
Animations by Deidre DeForest and Ken Becker
Graphic Design by Sherry Pribbenow

An Attainment Company Publication
© 2018 Attainment Company, Inc. All rights reserved.

Printed in the United States of America.

ISBN: 978-1-57861-286-4

Attainment Company

P.O. Box 930160
Verona, Wisconsin 53593-0160 USA
1-800-327-4269
www.AttainmentCompany.com

Contents

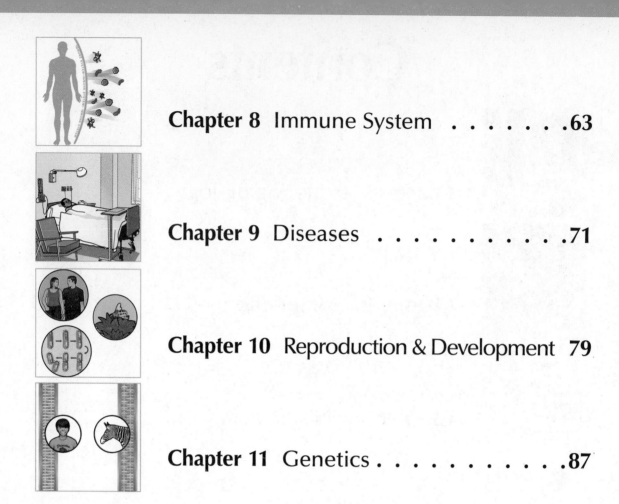

chapter
1

Exploring Biology

big ideas

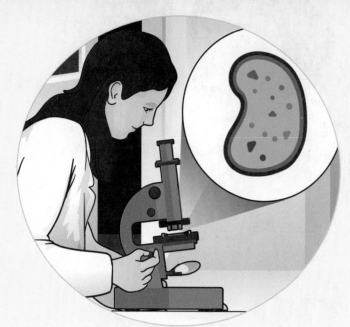

Scientists learn
by doing research.

Research can be
done in the laboratory
or in the field.

? Question

Hypothesis

Experiment

Data

Conclusion

A hypothesis comes
before an experiment.

Data is collected
during an experiment.

Exploring Biology

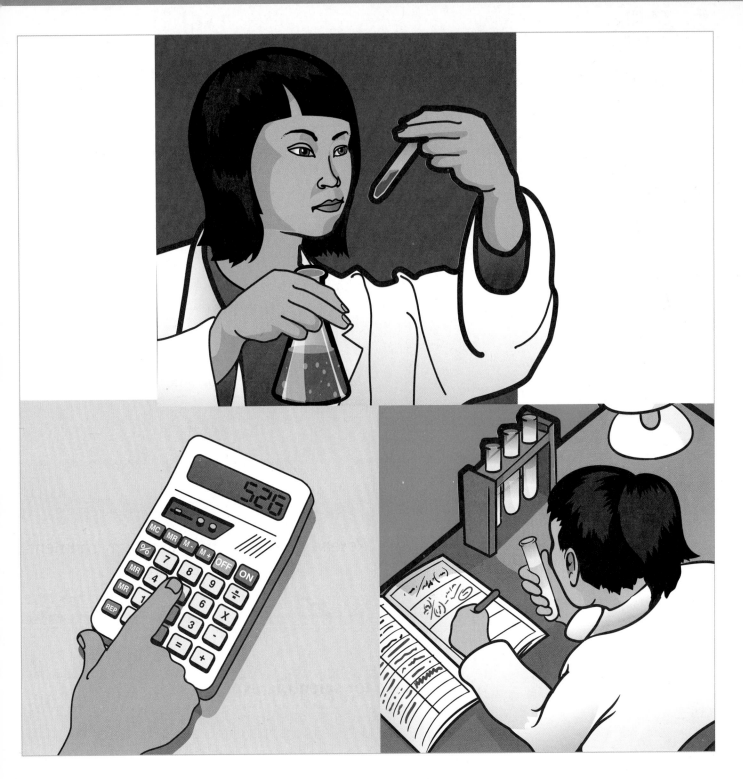

research — The process of attempting to learn new things.

experiment — A scientific procedure done to learn new things.

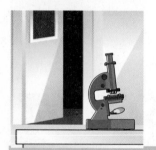

laboratory — A place designed for scientific *experiments*.

fieldwork — *Research* done in the natural environment.

FIND THE WORD

A place for scientific experiments.

— — — — — — — — — —

vocabulary

 Question

 Hypothesis

 Experiment

 Data

 Conclusion

scientific method The order of steps used in *research*.

conclusion What can be learned from an *experiment*.

hypothesis A guess about what will happen in an *experiment*.

data Numbers or facts collected from an *experiment*.

FIND THE WORD

Facts and numbers that are collected from an experiment.

___ ___ ___ ___

Student ? Questions:

1. (Circle) what happened when the thermometer was placed in the ice.

temperature increased   **temperature decreased**   **temperature didn't change**

2. (Circle) when a hypothesis should be made.

before an experiment   **during an experiment**   **after an experiment**

3. (Circle) what method the lab follows.

scientific method   **artistic method**   **water method**

Circle the correct answer.

1. Scientists learn by doing _____.

research  data   replication

2. Research can include laboratory experiments or _____.

conclusion  divide   fieldwork

3. A hypothesis comes _____ an experiment.

before   after  question

4. _____ is collected during experiments.

Hypothesis   Data  Variation

5. _____ are specially designed for scientific experiments.

Fieldwork  Laboratories  Ecosystems

6. A scientific procedure done to learn new things is an _____.

experiment  hypothesis  antibodies

7. The order of steps used in research is known as the _____.

conclusion   gene  scientific method

write about it

chapter 2

Competition

All organisms compete for
resources to survive.

Humans have a big
impact on ecosystems.

An animal that eats
another is
called a predator.

An animal that gets eaten
by another is called prey.

Competition

ecosystem   Community with organisms interacting with each other and nonliving things.

species   One type of an organism.

resources   Things required by an organism to survive.

biodiversity   Many *species* of organisms in an area.

One type of an organism.

__ __ __ __ __ __ __

vocabulary

herbivore   Animal that eats only plants.

carnivore   Animal that eats only meat.

predator   Animal that kills others for food.

prey   Animal that gets eaten by others as food.

It kills other animals for food.

___ ___ ___ ___ ___ ___ ___ ___

lab

Student ? Questions:

1. (Circle) which organism is at the top of its food chain.

        plants   **mouse**   **orca**

2. (Circle) how many organisms there are in each food chain.

        3   **4**   **10**

3. (Circle) the organism in the arctic food chain.

        polar bear   **hawk**   **lion**

quiz

Circle the correct answer.

1. All organisms _____ for resources to survive.

herbivore    compete    organelle

2. Humans have a big impact on _____.

ecosystems    energy    adaptation

3. An animal that eats another is known as a _____.

molecules 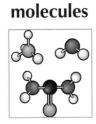   resources   predator

4. An animal that gets eaten by another is known as _____.

biodiversity    nutrients    prey

5. _____ are required by organisms to survive.

Resources  **Species**  **Disease**

6. An ecosystem with high _____ has many species in an area.

omnivore **biodiversity**  **sugar**

7. _____ eat only meat.

Herbivores  **Carnivores**  **DNA**

write about it

chapter 3

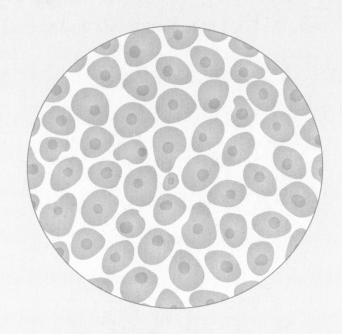

Cells and DNA

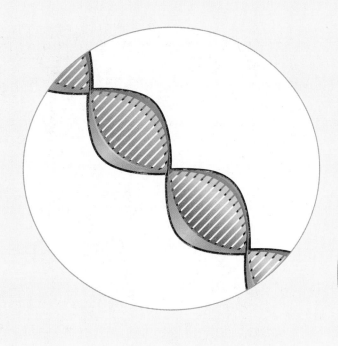

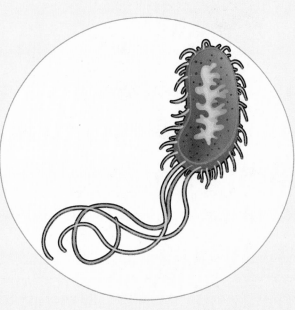

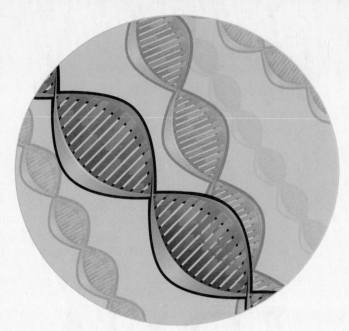

DNA is a code.

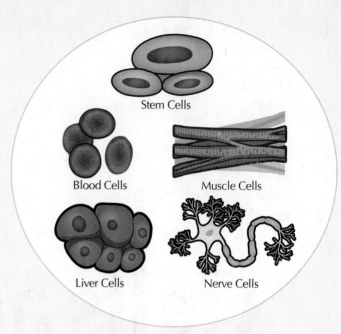

There are many types of cells.

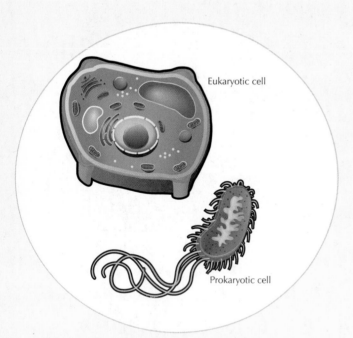

Eukaryotic cells are more complex than prokaryotic.

DNA makes everyone look different.

Cells and DNA

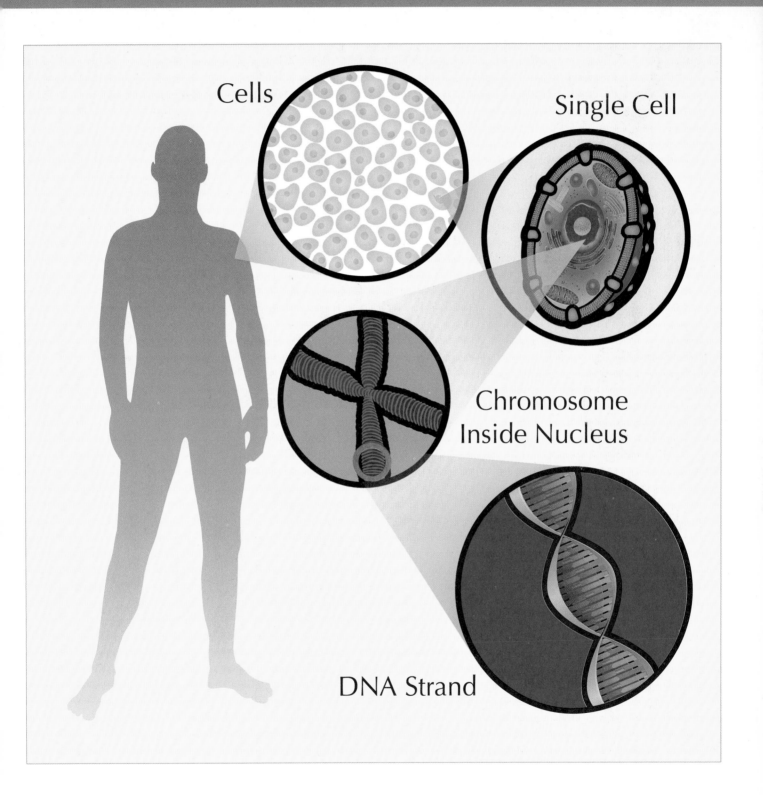

Cells

Single Cell

Chromosome
Inside Nucleus

DNA Strand

vocabulary

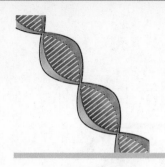

DNA   *Coded* instructions for a cell.

code   Information that needs to be translated.

eukaryotic   A more advanced type of cell.

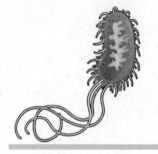

prokaryotic   A smaller and simpler type of cell.

A type of cell that is simpler and smaller.

__ __ __ __ __ __ __ __ __ __ __

vocabulary

organelle　　A part inside a cell with a function.

nucleus　　An *organelle* that controls a lot in a cell.

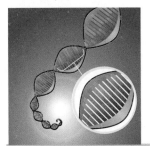

genes　　Sequences of *DNA* that determine characteristics in an organism.

bases　　The building blocks of *DNA*.

It's a part inside a cell and has a function.

— — — — — — — —

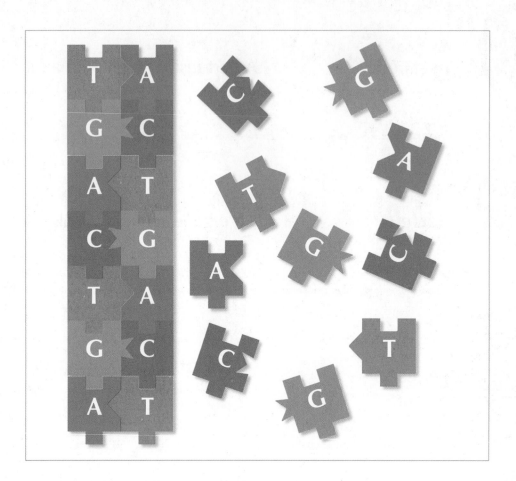

Student ? Questions:

1. (Circle) how many different bases of DNA there are.

       3   **4**   **10**

2. (Circle) what this lab uses to represent a DNA molecule.

    puzzle   **temperature**   **microscope**

3. (Circle) the letter that does not represent a DNA base.

    A   **G**   **M**

quiz

Circle the correct answer.

1. DNA is a _____.

organelle	code	pathogen

2. There are many types of _____.

mitosis	cells	nucleus
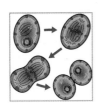		

3. _____ cells are more complex than prokaryotic cells.

Eukaryotic	DNA	Hypothesis

4. DNA makes everyone look _____.

prokaryotic	different	infection
		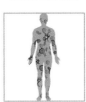

5. A _____ cell is a smaller and simpler type of cell.

organelle

heredity

prokaryotic

6. _____ are stretches of DNA that determine characteristics in an organism.

Genes

Nucleus

Vitamins

7. _____ are the building blocks of DNA.

Eukaryotic

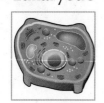

Bases

Vaccine

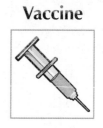

write about it

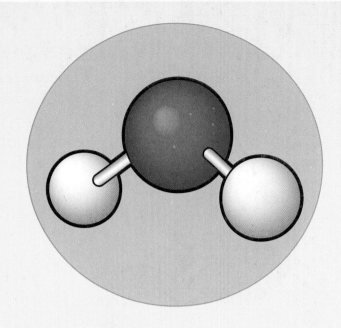

Molecules

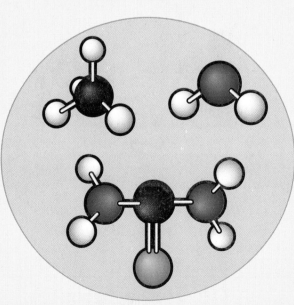

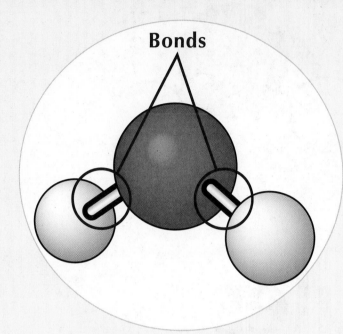

Bonds

Molecules are held together by bonds.

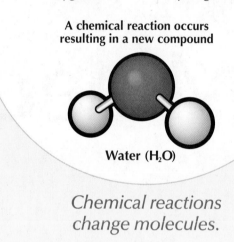

Oxygen (O) + **Hydrogen (H₂)**

A chemical reaction occurs resulting in a new compound

Water (H₂O)

Chemical reactions change molecules.

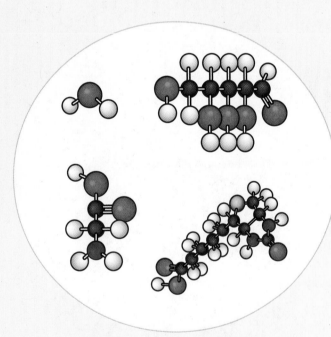

Different types of molecules are for different things.

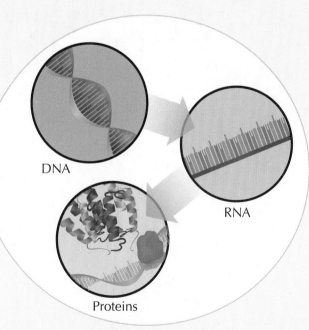

DNA

RNA

Proteins

DNA is a code for RNA and proteins.

Molecules

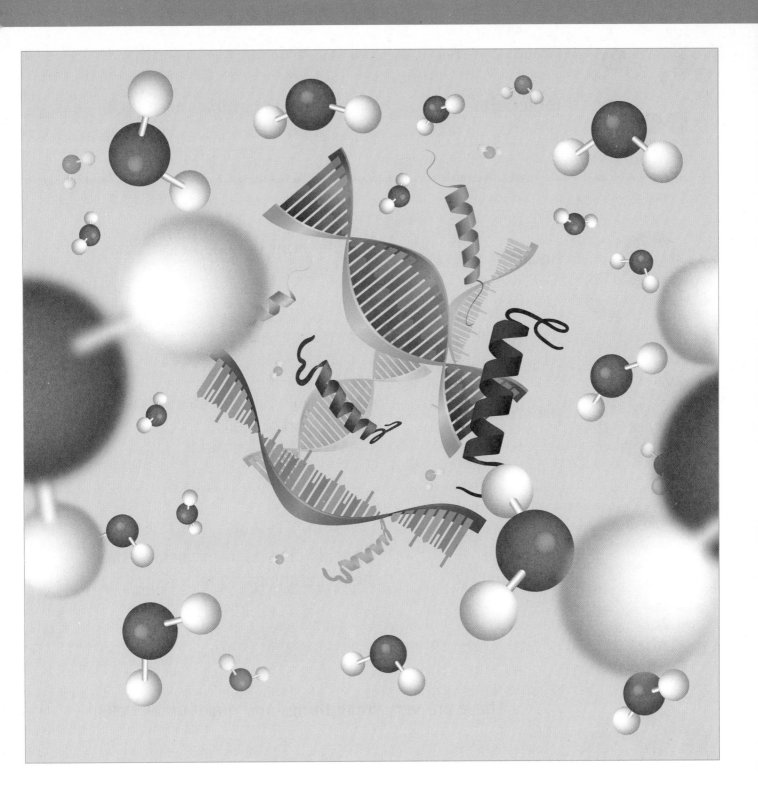

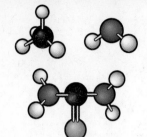

molecules

Very small things that make up all cells.

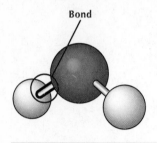

bonds

Connections between atoms that hold *molecules* together.

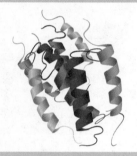

protein

Macromolecule that does most of the work in cells.

chemical reaction

Specific change to *molecules* that helps get things done

These are very small things and make up all cells.

— — — — — — — —

vocabulary

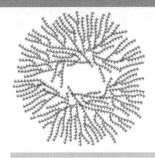

carbohydrate   Macromolecule that gives the cell *energy*.

energy   What makes the cell able to do things.

lipid   Macromolecule that makes up fat.

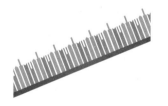

RNA   Macromolecule that acts as a code used to make *proteins*.

It makes the cell able to do things.

—— —— —— —— —— ——

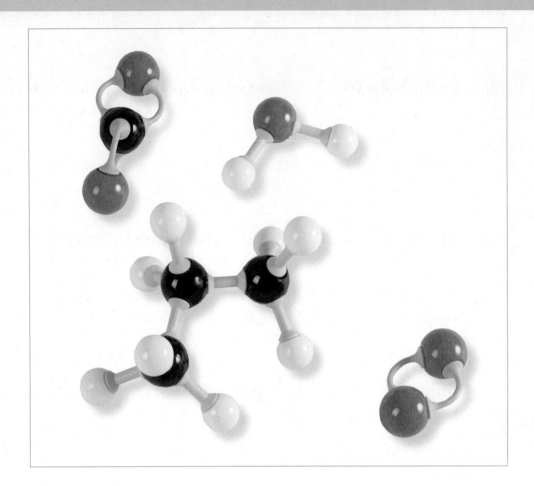

Student ? Questions:

1. (Circle) what happens when oil is mixed with water.

they mix together   **they don't mix together**   **the oil disappears**

2. (Circle) what the models represent.

molecules   **animals**   **cells**

3. (Circle) the amount of holes that the oxygen (red) atoms have.

0   **1**   **2**

quiz

Circle the correct answer.

1. Molecules are held together by _____.

species   bonds   chemical reaction

2. _____ change through chemical reactions.

Contagious   Energy   Molecules

   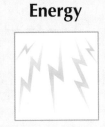   

3. Different types of molecules do _____ things in a cell.

DNA   different   predator

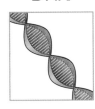      

4. DNA is a code for _____ and proteins.

RNA   energy   cure

5. _____ lead to specific changes to molecules that help get things done in a cell.

Chemical reactions

Lipids

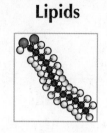

Vitamins

6. _____ makes the cell able to do things.

Carbon dioxide

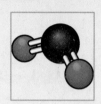

Punnett square

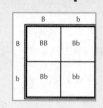

Energy

7. _____ are macromolecules that do most of the work in cells.

Water

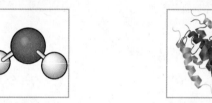

Proteins

Leaf

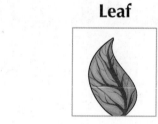

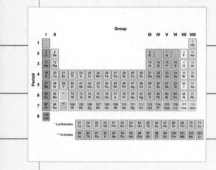

write about it

chapter 5

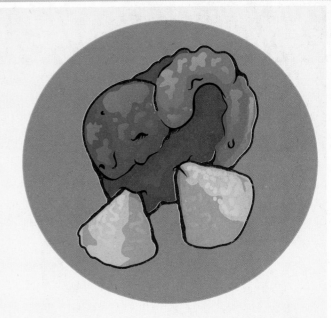

Cellular Respiration

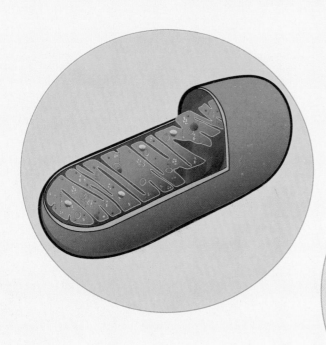

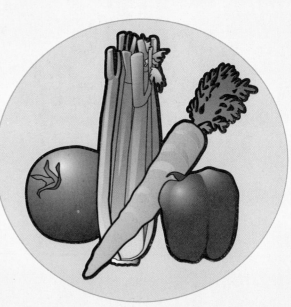

The body turns food into energy.

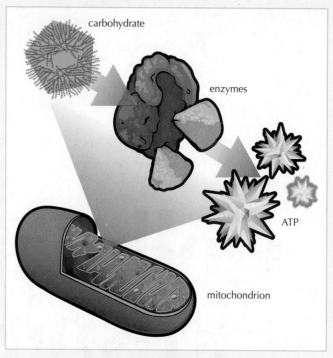

carbohydrate

enzymes

ATP

mitochondrion

Cellular respiration is performed mainly by the mitochondria.

ATP is the energy molecule.

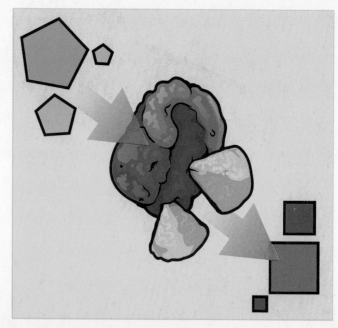

Enzymes cause chemical reactions.

Cellular Respiration

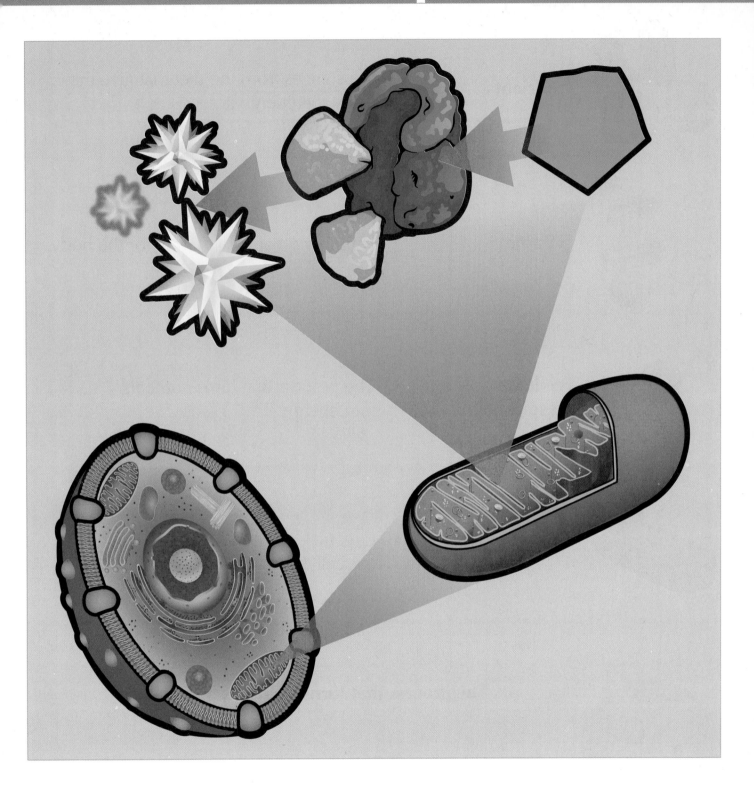

nutrients

Substances from the diet that give the body the energy it needs.

vitamin

A *nutrient* that is important for the body.

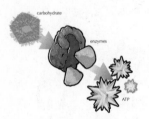

cellular respiration

The process that turns *nutrients* into energy.

mitochondria

Organelles that make energy for the cell to use.

FIND THE WORD

The process that turns nutrients into energy.

__ __ __ __ __ __ __ __ __

__ __ __ __ __ __ __ __ __ __ __

vocabulary

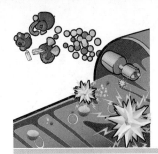

metabolism

The set of chemical reactions that give the cell the energy it needs.

ATP

The main molecule used as energy.

enzyme

A type of protein that makes chemical reactions happen.

fats

A *nutrient* that is necessary but can be unhealthy.

A type of protein that makes chemical reactions happen.

— — — — — —

lab

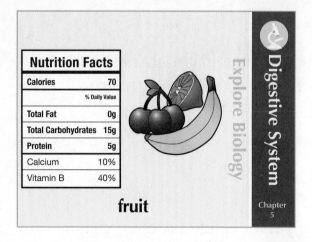

Nutrition Facts

Calories	70
% Daily Value	
Total Fat	0g
Total Carbohydrates	15g
Protein	5g
Calcium	10%
Vitamin B	40%

fruit

Explore Biology — Digestive System — Chapter 5

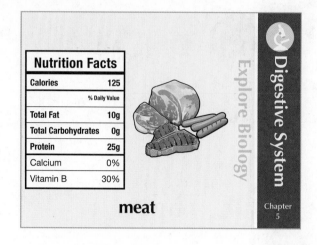

Nutrition Facts

Calories	125
% Daily Value	
Total Fat	10g
Total Carbohydrates	0g
Protein	25g
Calcium	0%
Vitamin B	30%

meat

Explore Biology — Digestive System — Chapter 5

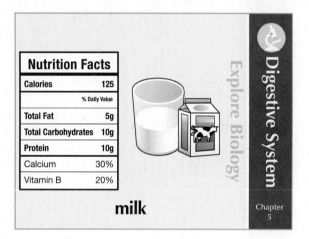

Nutrition Facts

Calories	125
% Daily Value	
Total Fat	5g
Total Carbohydrates	10g
Protein	10g
Calcium	30%
Vitamin B	20%

milk

Explore Biology — Digestive System — Chapter 5

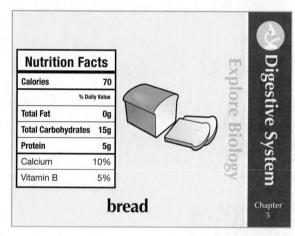

Nutrition Facts

Calories	70
% Daily Value	
Total Fat	0g
Total Carbohydrates	15g
Protein	5g
Calcium	10%
Vitamin B	5%

bread

Explore Biology — Digestive System — Chapter 5

Student ? Questions:

1. (Circle) the information that is not on food labels.

nutrition facts   **calories**   **mitochondria**

2. (Circle) the nutrient that is sometimes good and sometimes bad.

proteins   **vitamins**   **fat**

3. (Circle) the healthier food.

apple   **candy**   **chips**

quiz

1. The body turns _____ into energy.

enzymes

food

genetics

2. Cellular respiration is performed mainly by the _____.

bacteria

energy

mitochondria

3. ATP is the _____ molecule.

DNA

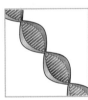

energy

infection

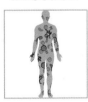

4. _____ cause chemical reactions.

Enzymes

Biodiversity

Disease

5. _____ are a type of nutrient that is needed by the body.

Variations   Lipids   Vitamins

6. _____ is a molecule that carries energy.

Carbon dioxide   ATP   Metabolism

7. Substances from the diet that give the body what it needs are called _____.

water   nutrients   photosynthesis

write about it

Photosynthesis

Plants do photosynthesis.

CO_2

Plants make food out of sunlight, CO_2, and water.

Plants need sunlight to grow.

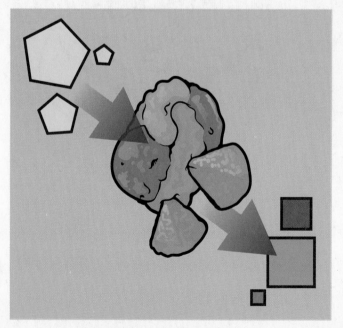

Photosynthesis is a chemical reaction.

Photosynthesis

plants   Mostly green organisms that make their own food.

photosynthesis   The process that *plants* use to make their own food.

sunlight   Energy that comes from the sun as light.

chloroplast   The organelle that performs *photosynthesis*.

FIND THE WORD

**They make their own food
and are mostly green organisms.**

— — — — — —

vocabulary

 **leaf** A flat, usually green, part of a *plant*.

 **growth** Increase in size.

 **convert** To make something change.

 **sugar** A sweet substance made of carbohydrates that gives organisms energy.

To make something change.

— — — — — — —

Student ? Questions:

1. (Circle) which is better for plants.

       no sunlight   **sunlight**   **no water**

2. (Circle) the group of plants that grew better.

       in the light   **in the dark**   **neither**

3. (Circle) the color of the plant when it grows.

       blue   **red**   **green**

1. _____ do photosynthesis.

Plants

Antibodies

Humans

2. Plants make _____ out of sunlight, CO_2, and water.

bacteria

food

convert

3. Plants need sunlight to _____.

grow

sugar

mitosis

4. _____ is a chemical reaction.

Chromosome

Photosynthesis

Sunlight

5. _____ are the organelles that perform photosynthesis.

| Phases | Growth | Chloroplasts |

6. _____ are the flat and usually green part of plants.

| Water | Sugar | Leaves |

7. Energy that comes from the sun as light is known as _____.

| sunlight | plants | embryo |

write about it

chapter
7

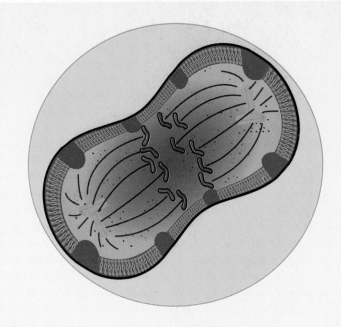

Cell Division

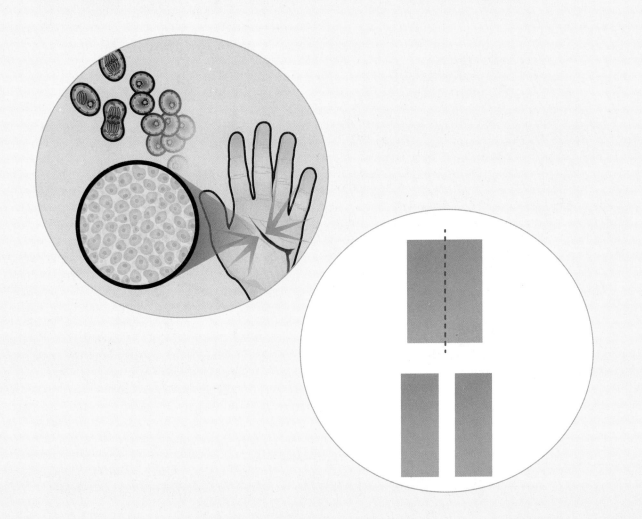

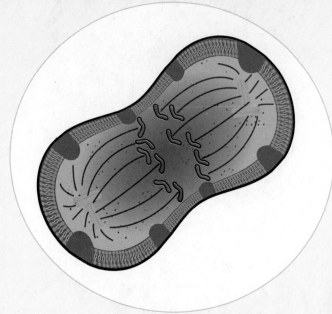

Most cells split through mitosis.

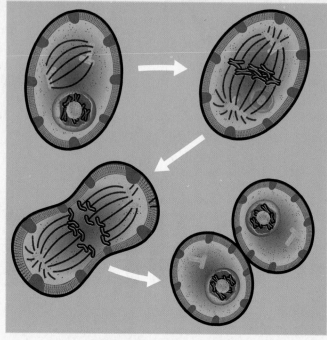

Mitosis has many phases.

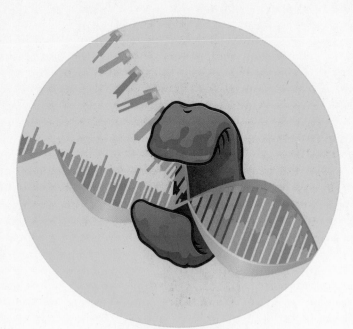

The DNA is copied by DNA Polymerase before division.

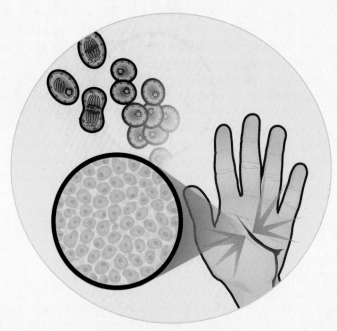

Cells divide for growth and repair.

Cell Division

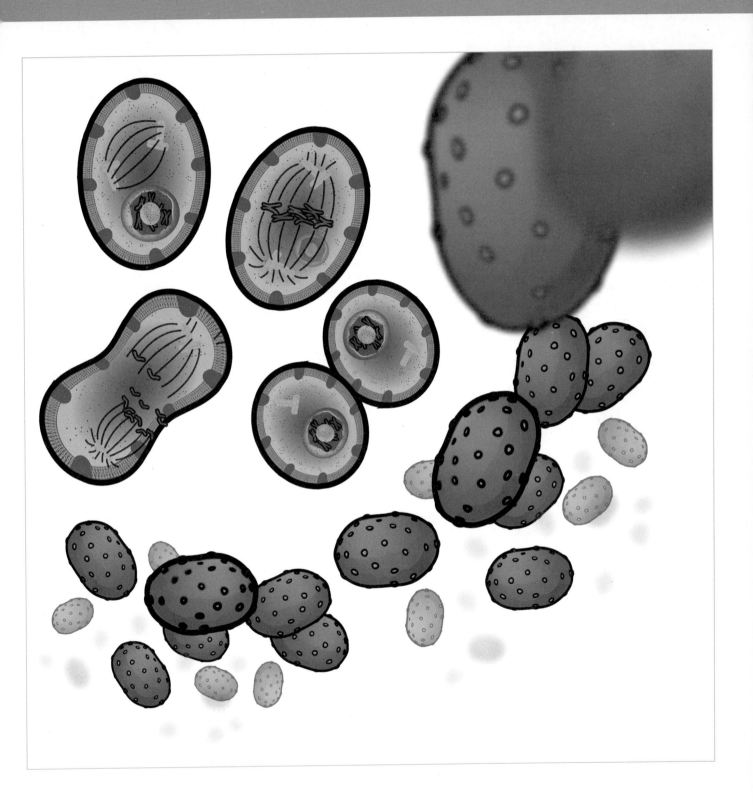

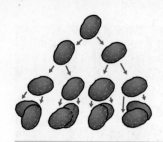

reproduce To create new organisms.

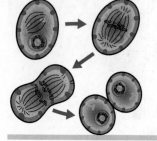

mitosis The major type of cell division in larger organisms.

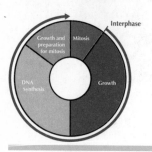

cell cycle A series of events that leads to cell division.

divide To split in two.

To create new organisms.

— — — — — — — — — —

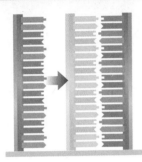

replication — Copying.

DNA polymerase — Protein responsible for the *replication* of DNA.

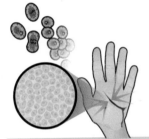

repair — To fix when there is an issue.

phase — One part of a process.

One part of a process.

— — — — —

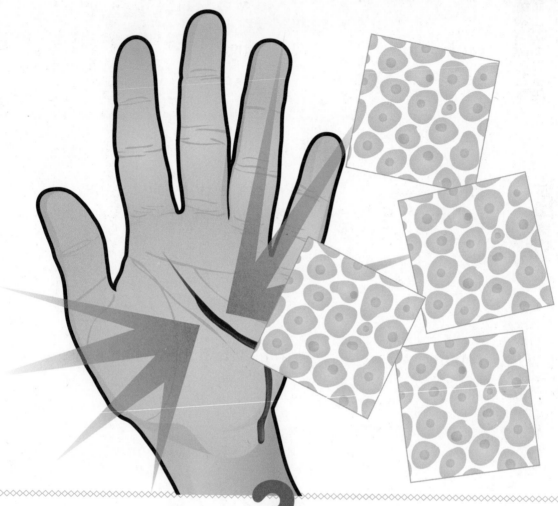

Student **?** Questions:

1. (Circle) what happens to the number of cells during cell division.

      increases   **decreases**   **stays the same**

2. (Circle) which of the following is not a reason for cell division to occur.

      growth   **repair**   **mitochrondria**

3. (Circle) how many cells there are after one cycle of division.

      zero   **one**   **two**

1. Most cells split through _____.

| antibodies | mitosis | biodiversity |

 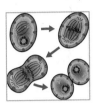

2. Before division, _____ is copied by DNA polymerase.

| DNA | nutrients | phase |

3. Cells divide for _____ and repair.

| growth | muscle | mitosis |

 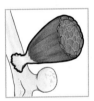 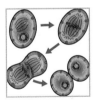

4. Mitosis has many _____.

| phases | repair | symptoms |

5. The _____ consists of a series of events that leads to cell division.

reproduce

bonds

cell cycle

6. When a cell _____ it divides in two.

mitochondria

DNA polymerase

divides

7. Each part of the mitosis process is called a _____.

phase

growth

chloroplast

write about it

chapter
8

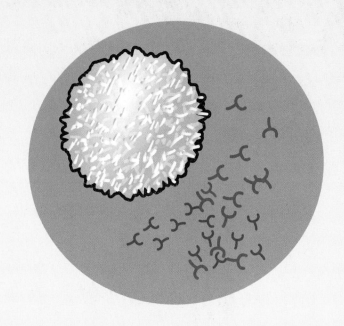

Immune System

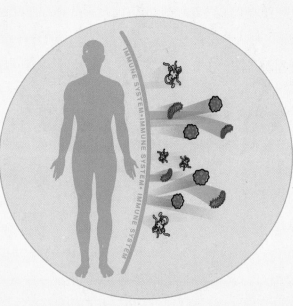

The immune system keeps the body healthy.

Germs can make you sick.

Germs are everywhere.

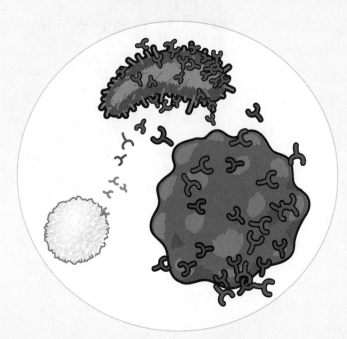

Antibodies help fight germs.

Immune System

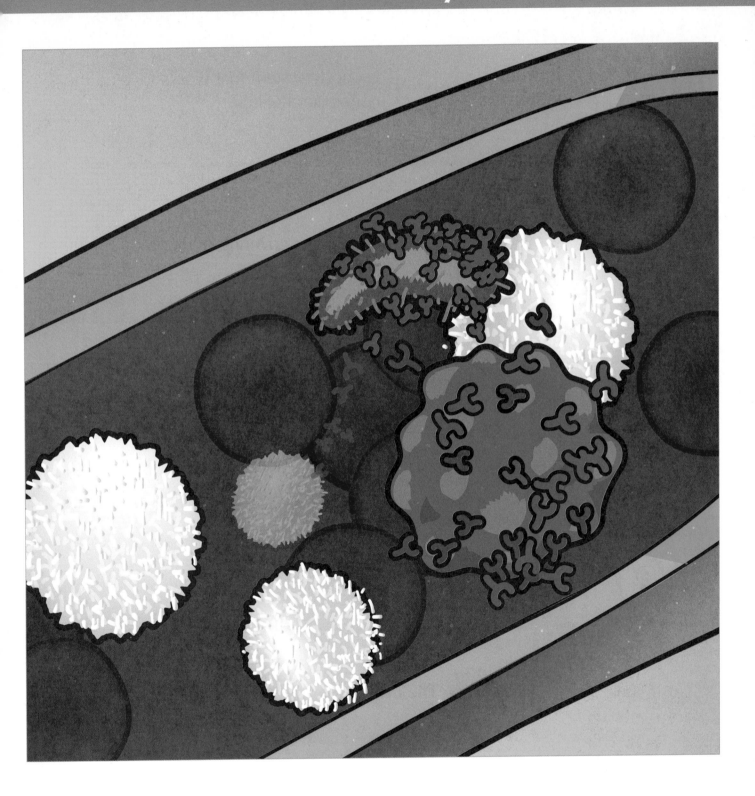

immune system

A body system that works to keep the organism healthy.

skin

The outer covering of the body.

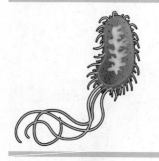

bacteria

Common microscopic organisms.

viruses

Very small things that often cause *infections*.

The outer covering of your body.

FIND THE WORD

___ ___ ___ ___

infection

When a virus or microorganism enters the body.

fever

An increase in body temperature when sick.

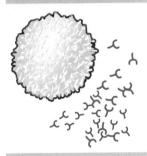

antibodies

Proteins that help get rid of *infections*.

allergies

A dangerous immune response to a safe substance.

Proteins that help get rid of infections.

__ __ __ __ __ __ __ __ __ __

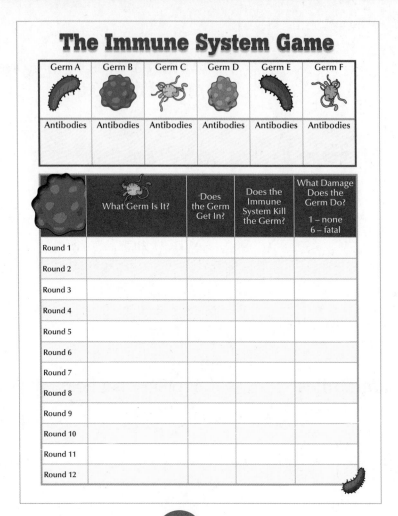

The Immune System Game

	Germ A	Germ B	Germ C	Germ D	Germ E	Germ F
	Antibodies	Antibodies	Antibodies	Antibodies	Antibodies	Antibodies

	What Germ Is It?	Does the Germ Get In?	Does the Immune System Kill the Germ?	What Damage Does the Germ Do? 1 – none 6 – fatal
Round 1				
Round 2				
Round 3				
Round 4				
Round 5				
Round 6				
Round 7				
Round 8				
Round 9				
Round 10				
Round 11				
Round 12				

Student ? Questions:

1. (Circle) which of the following is not a germ.

bacteria   viruses   antibodies

2. (Circle) the job of the immune system.

help us think   help us move   keep us healthy

3. (Circle) what can happen when germs invade the body.

biodiversity   infection   eukaryote

quiz

Circle the correct answer.

1. The _____ system keeps the body healthy.

musculoskeletal	hypothesis	immune
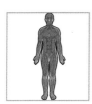		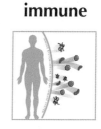

2. _____ can make you sick.

Germs	Nutrients	Biodiversity

3. Germs are _____.

antibodies	nucleus	everywhere

4. _____ help fight germs.

Infection	Antibodies	Punnett square
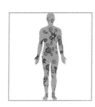		

5. A dangerous immune response to a safe substance happens in people with _____.

allergies    resources 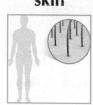   skin

6. _____ are very small things that often cause infections.

Vitamins   Viruses    Fever

7. An _____ occurs when a virus or microorganism enters the body.

infection   ATP   allergies

write about it

chapter
9

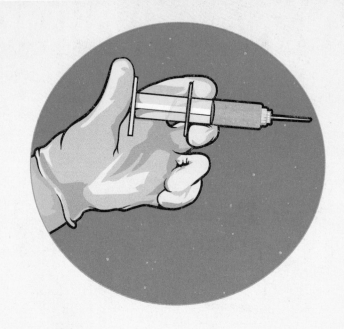

Diseases

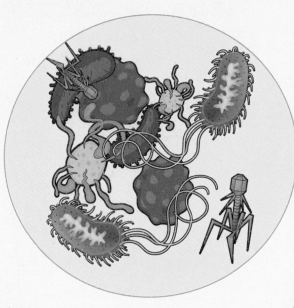

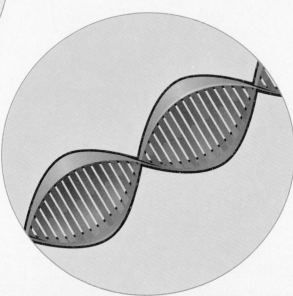

big ideas

Diseases are dangerous and can be fatal.

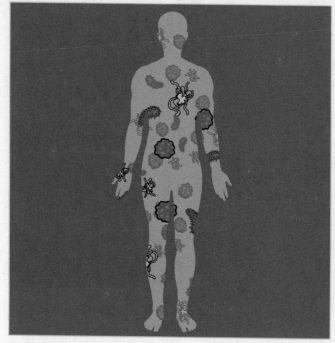

Diseases often come from infections.

Cancer is a disease.

Some diseases can be cured.

Diseases

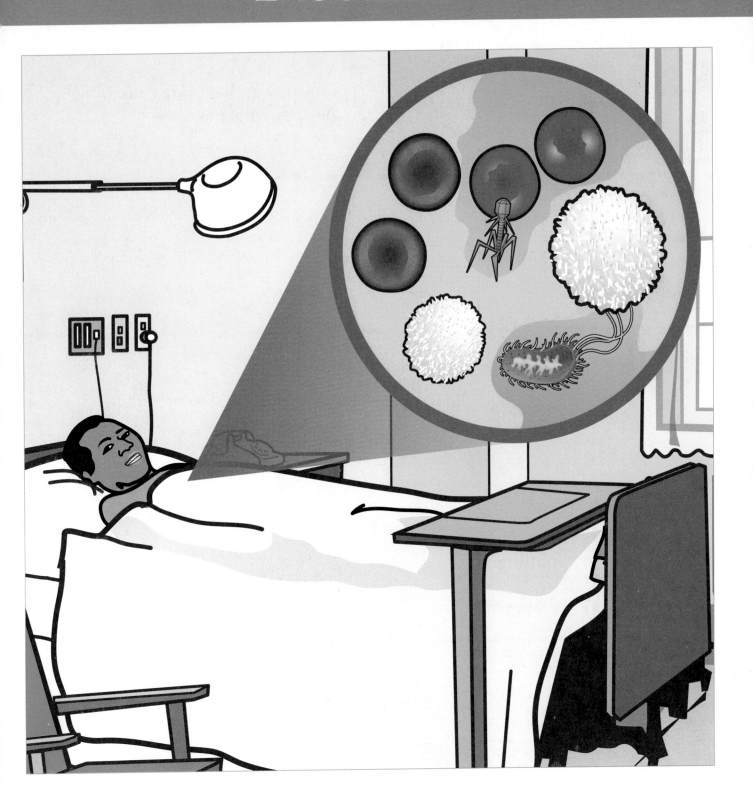

disease — A problem with the body caused by an infection or genes.

symptom — A physical problem caused by a disease.

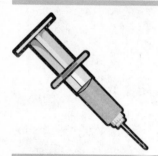

vaccine — Substance designed to protect us from a future disease.

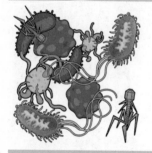

pathogen — Something that invades the body and can make us sick.

FIND THE WORD

Something that invades the body and can make us sick.

— — — — — — — —

vocabulary

fatal　　　　Results in death.

contagious　　　　Able to be passed on to someone else.

cancer　　　　A common *disease* where cells divide without control.

cure　　　　A way to get rid of a *disease*.

A way to get rid of a disease.

___ ___ ___ ___

lab

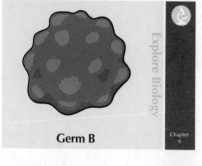

Germ B

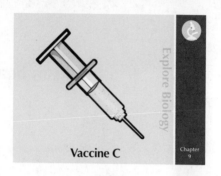

Vaccine C

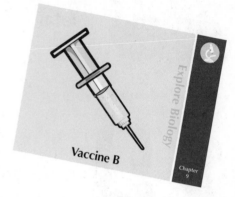

Vaccine B

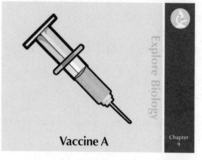

Vaccine A

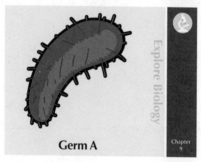

Germ A

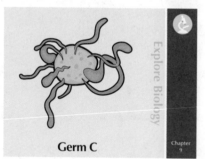

Germ C

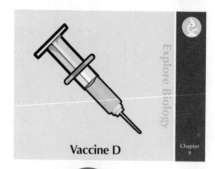

Vaccine D

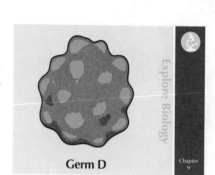

Germ D

Student ? Questions:

1. (Circle) which germ you are protected from with Vaccine B.

        germ A   **germ B**   **germ E**

2. (Circle) how many germ cards there are.

        4   **5**   **6**

3. (Circle) how many vaccine cards there are.

        4   **5**   **6**

Circle the correct answer.

1. _____ are dangerous and can be fatal.

Antibodies

Cure

Diseases

2. Diseases often come from _____.

skin

infections

vaccines

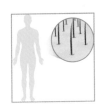 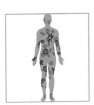 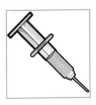

3. _____ is a disease.

Cancer

Photosynthesis

Protein

  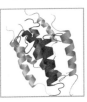

4. Some diseases can be _____.

resources

organelles

cured

5. _____ are physical problems caused by a disease.

Symptoms

Pathogen

Cellular respiration

6. _____ are designed to prevent people from getting diseases.

Vaccines

Cancer

Fever

7. A _____ disease can be passed on to someone else.

embryo

contagious

symptom

write about it

chapter 10

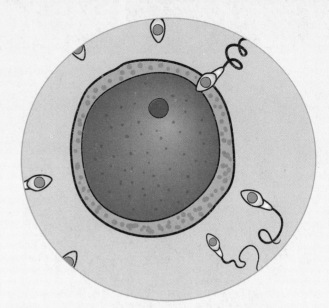

Reproduction and Development

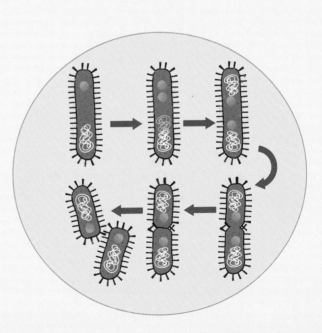

Humans use sexual reproduction to reproduce.

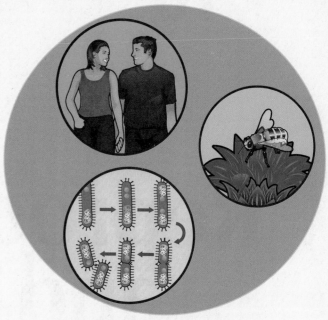

Organisms reproduce in different ways.

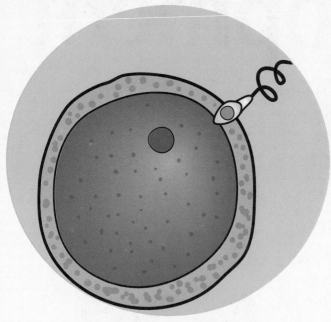

A sperm and an egg come together during fertilization.

DNA controls human development.

Reproduction & Development

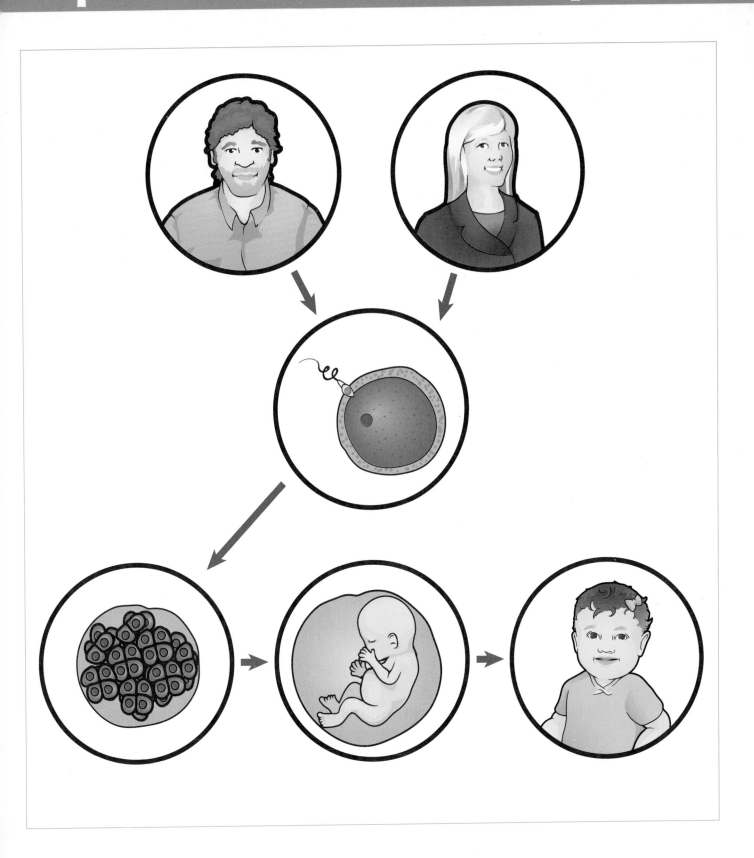

vocabulary

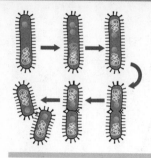

asexual

A type of reproduction that doesn't use gametes.

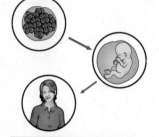

development

Progress through the stages of turning into an adult.

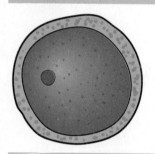

egg

Gamete produced by a female organism that is needed for reproduction.

sperm

Gamete produced by a male organism that is needed for reproduction.

FIND THE WORD

Gamete produced by a female organism that is needed for reproduction.

___ ___ ___

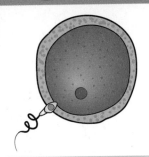

fertilization Joining of an *egg* and *sperm* that starts *development*.

pregnancy The time where a baby develops before being born.

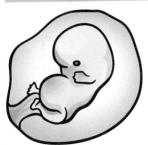

embryo Very early stage of *development* during *pregnancy*.

differentiation Turning into different types of cells.

The time where a baby develops before being born.

—— —— —— —— —— —— —— —— ——

1.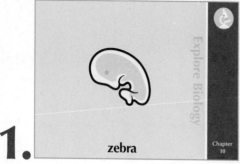
zebra

2.
zebra

3.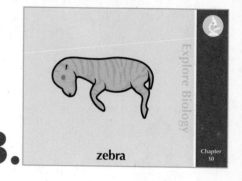
zebra

4.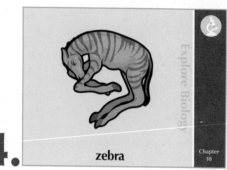
zebra

5.
zebra

Student ? Questions:

1. Circle the animal that is not included in the development cards.

zebra   **bear**   **fish**

2. Circle the last stage of development.

reproduction   **adulthood**   **birth**

3. Circle what each creature in the development cards has in common.

they are all animals   **they are all plants**   **they are bacteria**

Circle the correct answer.

1. _____ use sexual reproduction to reproduce.

Humans	Food	Bacteria

2. Organisms _____ in different ways.

hypothesis	molecules	reproduce
	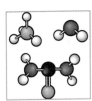	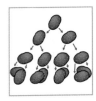

3. A sperm and an egg combine for _____.

fertilization	asexual	infection
	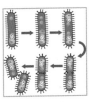	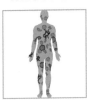

4. _____ controls human development.

DNA	Photosynthesis	Disease
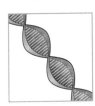		

5. _____ is the male gamete, and it is needed for reproduction.

Pregnancy   Sperm   Carnivore

6. _____ is the time where a baby develops before being born.

Carbohydrate   Carbon dioxide   Pregnancy

7. An _____ exists at a very early stage of development during pregnancy.

fatal   embryo   asexual

write about it

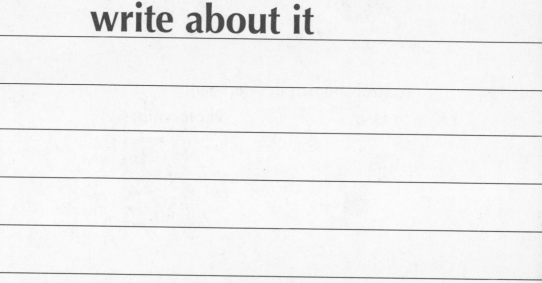

chapter 11

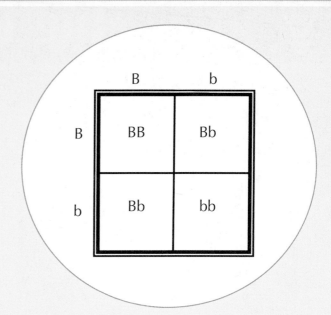

Genetics

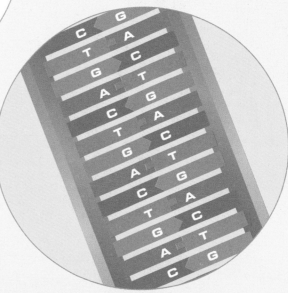

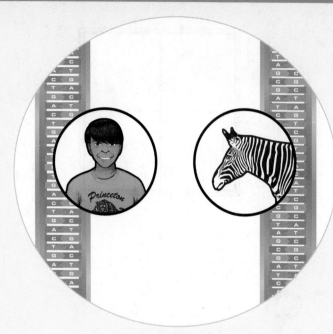

Organisms look
the way they do
because of genetics.

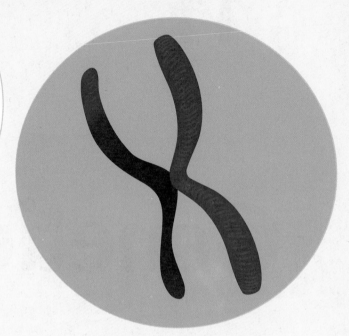

Genes are organized
into chromosomes.

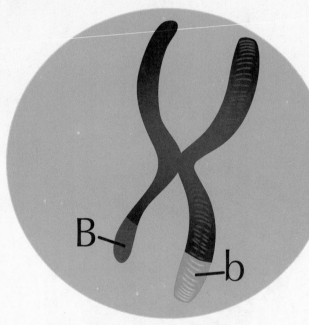

A person has two
alleles for every gene.

If one allele is dominant,
a dominant trait
will be expressed.

Genetics

traits   Characteristics that make a person unique.

variation   Differences.

chromosomes   Structures of DNA and protein that carry genetic information.

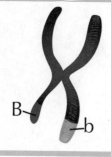

allele   One form of a gene.

FIND THE WORD

One form of a gene.

__ __ __ __ __ __

 **dominant** Only needs one *allele* to be expressed.

 **recessive** Requires both *alleles* to be expressed.

  heredity Passing *traits* to offspring.

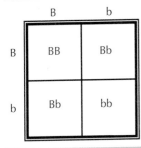 **Punnett square** Diagram used to see the chance of passing on certain traits.

Passing traits to offspring.

— — — — — — — — —

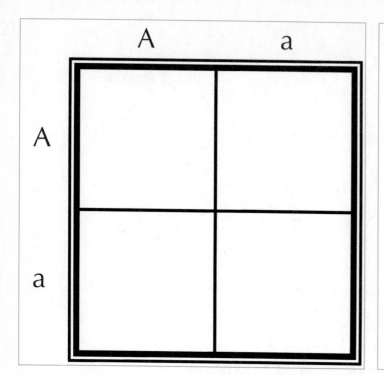

Student ? Questions:

1. (Circle) the tool used to learn about genetics.

    Punnett square   **hammer**   **trees**

2. (Circle) the letter that represents a dominant allele.

      a   **b**   **B**

3. (Circle) the letter that represents a recessive allele.

      a   **A**   **B**

quiz

Circle the correct answer.

1. Organisms look the way they do because of _____.

data   genetics   Punnett square

 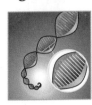 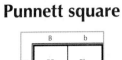

2. Genes are organized into _____.

nutrients   variation   chromosomes

3. A person has two alleles for every _____.

recessive   muscle   gene

 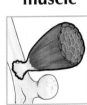 

4. If a person has a dominant allele, a _____ trait will be expressed.

dominant   prey   chromosome

5. In genetics, _____ means differences.

trait

variation

cell cycle

6. When a trait requires two of the same allele to be expressed, it is a _____ trait.

recessive

nucleus

dominant

7. When parents pass traits to their offspring, it is called _____.

development

allele

heredity

write about it

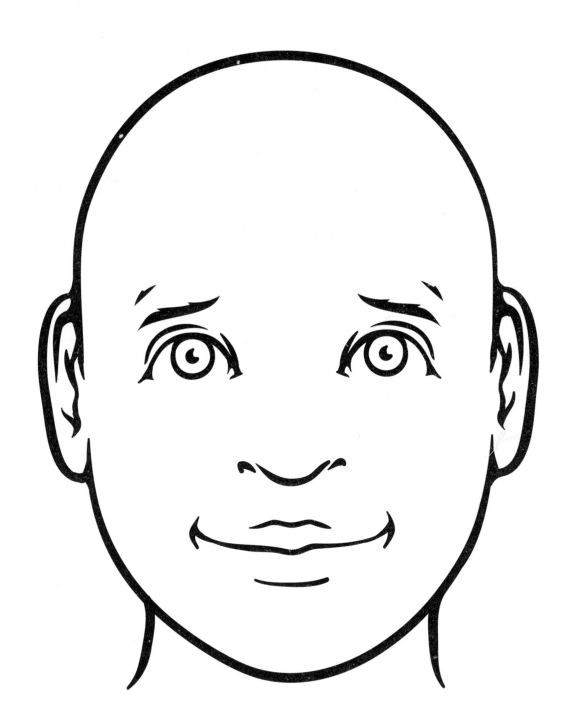

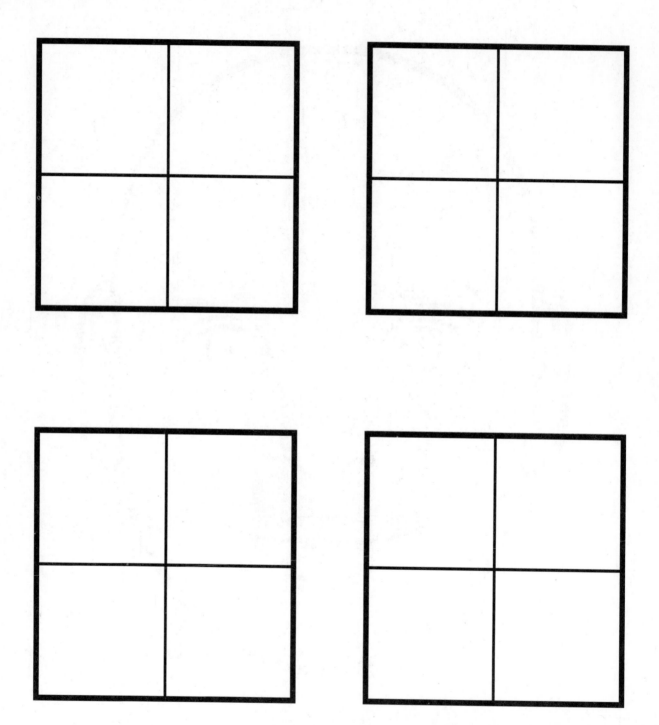